YORRIK

PUBLISHED 1990 by Printwise Publications Limited
47 Bradshaw Road, Tottington, BURY, Lancs BL8 3PW.

Warehouse & Orders:
41 Willan Ind. Estate, Vere Street (off Eccles New Road)
SALFORD M5 2GR
061-745 9168

ISBN 1 872226 05 1

Printed and bound by Manchester Free Press, Paragon Mill, Jersey Street, Manchester M4 6FP.
Tel. 061-236 8822.

Additional Material organised by

Cliff Hayes

Additional typesetting by Alan Griffith, Bournemouth Home for the Typographically Insane

Many thanks must go to the Home for the Befuddled for letting Billy and Wally out on a day pass to finish the book. Also the Yorrik Appreciation Society for not threatening to knee-cap us! and of course Yorrik and his family for not making any 'bones' about it.

Introduction

During 1988 we had on our Radio Programme on Radio Merseyside a "Comedy Caption" competition where we gave out a situation and the listeners telephoned in with their funny lines. These became a talking point all over Merseyside. One character especially came up time and time again: Yorrik!

This was the character that seemed to fire a lot of imaginations. One situation was Hamlet staring at Yorrik and the classic line from Yorrik "It's the last time I'm going self-catering with you". From then on the loveable skull became a major part of comedy captions.

Everyone has their favourite Yorrik line. Wally likes "Aar Ay." when Yorrik got a sunbed for his birthday, Billy likes the football match where Yorrick was heard to shout "Don't forget to keep the ball on the floor". It was these hilarious lines that inspired the two illustrators to turn the ones they remembered best, and some of their own into this book. We have had many laughs over these and think that it is another winner from these two Merseyside Artists who have a great deal of talent (they did our first Billy & Wally Joke Book).

We are only too pleased to write this introduction, and hope that you enjoy this book as much as we have.

WALLY SCOTT

BILLY BUTLER

"I'm made-up with this book, it hasn't called me slaphead once!"

YORRIK

THE ADVENTURES OF YORRIK

WRITTEN & DRAWN BY ANDREW & BERNARD GALBRAITH

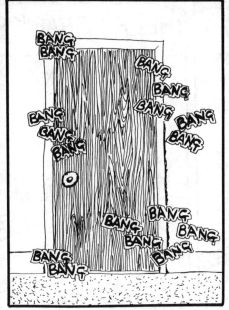

A SPOT OF BAD LUCK

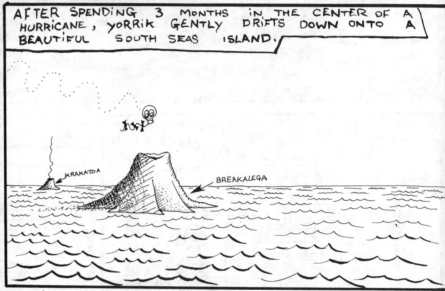

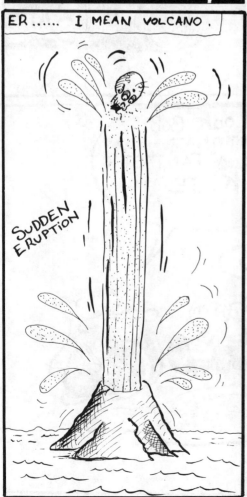

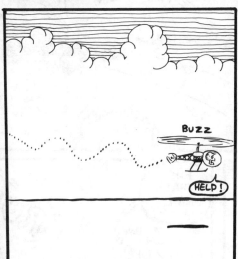

SUPER SKULL

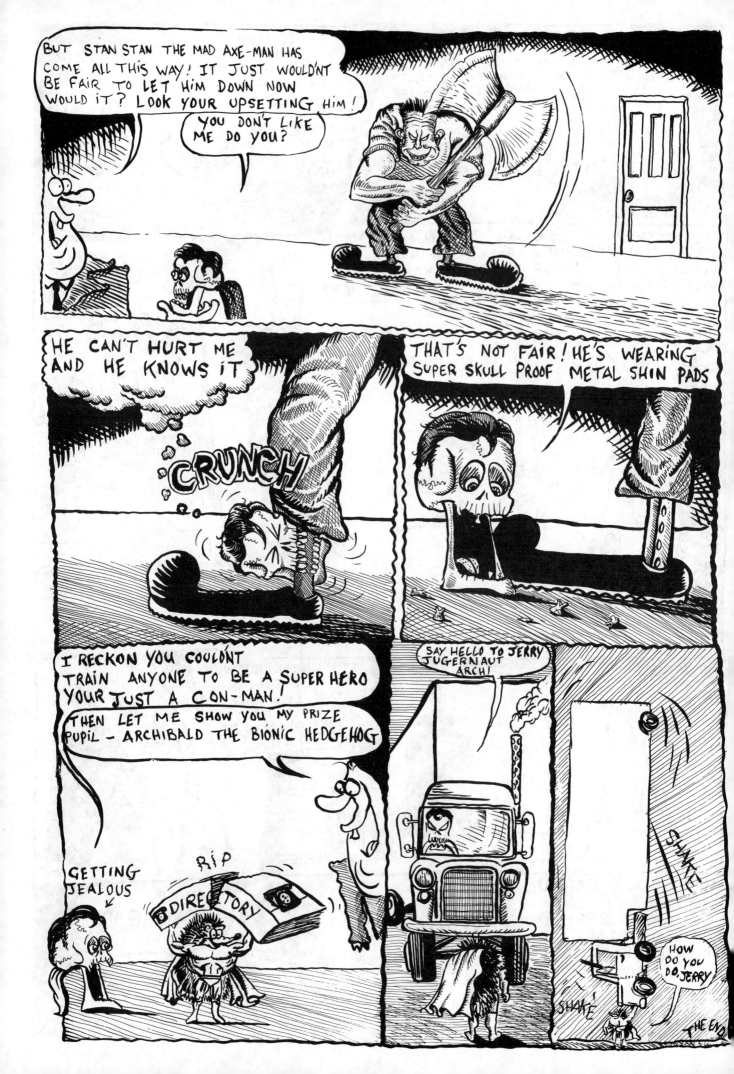

THE DRIVING TEST

YORRIK WILL YOU HURRY UP WE'RE GOING TO BE LATE

HURRY UP, HURRY UP, YORRIK! WILL YOU HURRY UP? COME ON, COME ON, COME ON! HURRY, HURRY, HURRY. WILL YOU SHIFT YOURSELF!

WILL YA SHUT IT WOMAN!!! YOUR GOING TO MAKE ME CUT — MYSELF!

YORRIK is 008

DEEP IN THE HEART OF M.I.5.

YORRIK I HAVE AN IMPORTANT MISSION FOR YOU. COME WITH ME, I'LL TAKE YOU TO "Q."

BUS STOP

I DIDN'T THINK YOU MEANT THIS TYPE OF — QUEUE.

I DIDN'T

YOUR MISSION IS OF NATIONAL IMPORTANCE, WE HAVE UNCOVERED A PLOT THAT A VILLAIN IS GOING TO EXPLODE AN ATOMIC BOMB IN THE ACME FISH CENTER — WHICH DISTRIBUTES FISH TO EVERY CHIPPY IN ENGLAND. IF HE SUCCEEDS THE NATION WOULD BE RUINED.

THIS IS Q — HE'LL GIVE YOU HIS LATEST INVENTIONS TO OVERTHROW THE VILLAIN.

IS THIS MY NEW CAR? CAN'T I HAVE AN ASTON MARTIN?

WHAT'S WRONG WITH A ROLLER?

TALENT SHOW

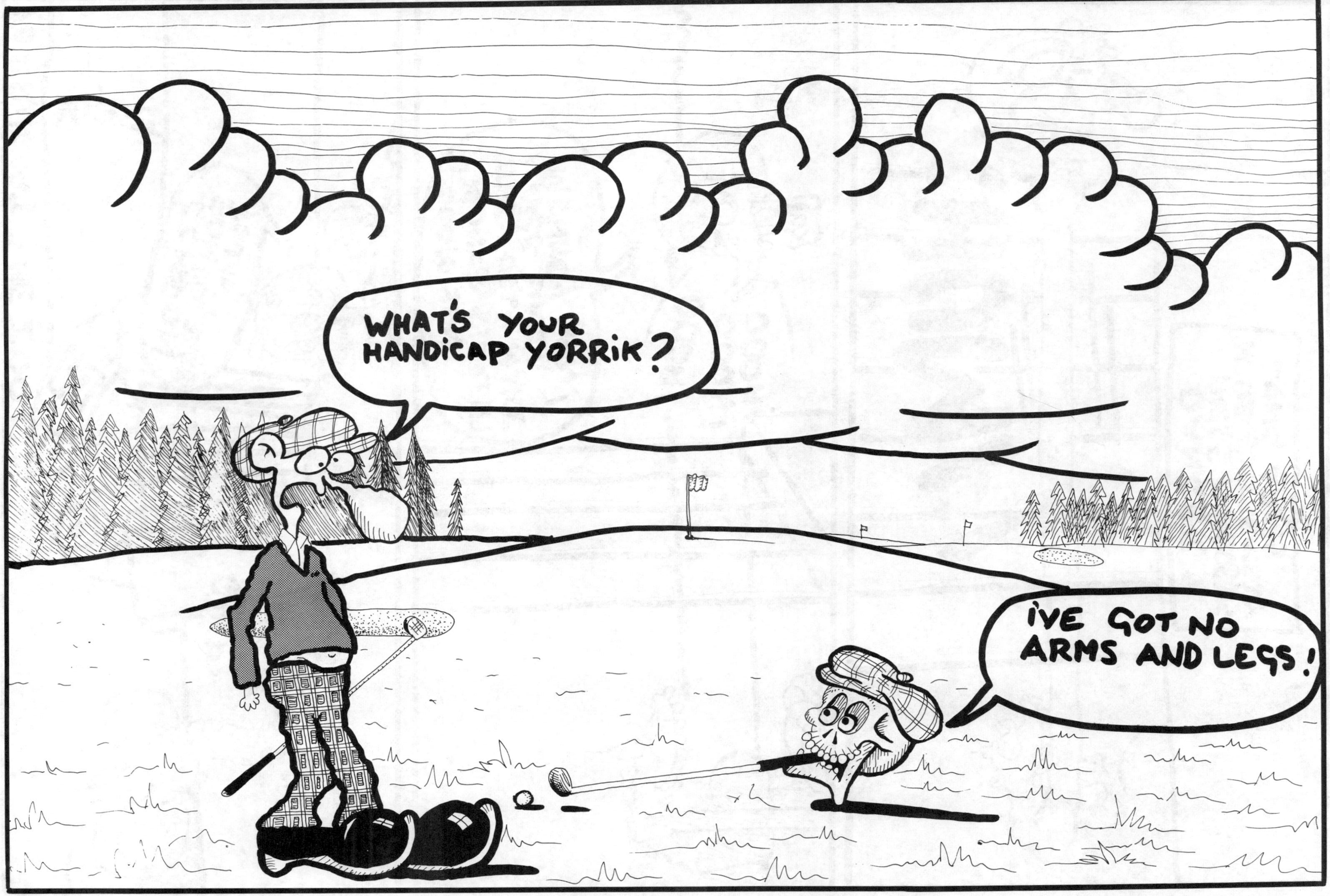
WHAT'S YOUR HANDICAP YORRIK?
I'VE GOT NO ARMS AND LEGS!

COUNT YORRICULA
DEEP IN THE HEART OF TRANSYLVANIA LIES A VILLAGE SHROUDED IN TERROR. FOR CENTURIES IT HAS BEEN FREE OF ITS CURSE - A CURSE THAT HAS BECOME A LEGEND BUT THIS QUIET VILLAGE STILL SITS IN THE MENACING SHADOW OF CASTLE YORRICULA. SOON THE LEGEND WILL BECOME REALITY AGAIN!
HELLS TEETH I'VE OVERSLEPT
RNG
NEXT MORNING A STRANGE SICKNESS HITS THE VILLAGE MAIDENS
HMM ITS JUST LIKE ALL THE OTHERS... BODY DRAINED OF BLOOD AND TWO WIERD PUNCTURE MARKS ON HER ANKLE, LOOKS LIKE A CASE OF VAMPIRISM!
OH PULL THE OTHER ONE, DOC
COME ON WE'VE GOT TO DESTROY YORRICULA!
GET OFF I'M NOT GOING ANYWHERE NEAR THAT PLACE
IM FROM ACME DOUBLE GLAZING I HAVE AN APPOINTMENT TO SEE YOUR MASTER CAN I COME IN
SURE MAN
THATS HIM OVER THERE IN THAT BOX, HOW ABOUT A NICE CUP OF TEA?
SO KIND
WELL THAT WAS EASY ENOUGH
OH DEAR!
GLUMP
I DON'T THINK SO
MIND YOUR HEAD
WELL IF A STAKE THROUGH THE HEART HAS NO EFFECT WHAT ABOUT SUNLIGHT?
SWISH
NO PROBLEM!
NOW PREPARE TO DIE!
DUCK
WHAT ABOUT RUNNING WATER DOES THAT KILL VAMPIRES?
I'M AFRAID SO!

HERE'S YORRIK THE MOST AMAZING STUNTMAN THE WORLD HAS EVER SEEN.

TODAY HE IS GOING TO JUMP 650 BUSES ON HIS SUPER-CHARGED ROLLER-SKATE

HE'S JUST NEARING THE RAMP ....

AND HE'S AWAY 5,6,7, ...

.... 648, 649, 650. HE'S DONE IT!

SMASH!

BUS STOP

646   647   648   649   650

THE ADVENTURES OF YORRIKS EYEBALL

IM BORED OF JUST BEING YORRIKS EYEBALL IM OFF TO SEE THE WORLD

COME BACK

THIS IS THE LIFE, FREE AT LAST, ITS A BIT TIRING, ALL THIS JIGGING ABOUT. I THINK ILL GO IN THIS PUB!

PANT PANT

A FEW HOURS LATER

ROLL OUT THE BARRA!

HIC! HIC!

EYE, EYE, WHATS GOING ON HERE OH, NO ITS A HOLD-UP!

BANK

BANG!

HELP POLICE THERES JUST BEEN A HOLD UP IN THE HIGH STREET

THERE HAS? ARE YOU AN EYE-WITNESS

YES, IM AN EYE BALL

DRUNK! OBVIOUSLY - A HOAX!

DING!

BANK   GROCERS

THE CROOKS ARE GETTING AWAY! WHAT A STROKE OF LUCK A GROCERS, EVERYONE KNOWS CARROTS GIVE EYES EXTRA STRENGTH

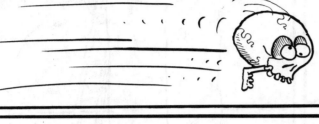

Caption Competition

....

....

NAME ....

ADDRESS ....

POST CODE .... DAYTIME PHONE NO ....

Above is a cartoon featuring three of Merseyside's best known characters. Can you give the cartoon a comic caption? What is Wally saying to Yorrik or what is Billy saying to Wally. Write yourself a caption in the space provided and send to:

Billy & Wally Caption Competition
Radio Merseyside
55 Paradise Street
LIVERPOOL L13 BP

The deadly duo will be judging the captions (as soon as Wally has recovered from the Miss Hold Your Plums Contest) and prizes are offered for the best and funniest.

NAME

ADDRESS

POST CODE .... DAYTIME PHONE Nr.

Above is a cartoon featuring Byron (My cousin) and Billy Bragg of Barnes. Can you are the cartoon to a caption? What is Wally saying to York? or what is Billy saying to York? Write yourself a caption in the space provided and send to

Black, White Cartoon Competition,
Radio Merseyside,
55 Paradise Stree,
Liverpool L3 9l

The competition will begin ... continue and soon as Wally has begun and the Blue Note 'Joust Jack Cartoon' has place a captioned in the best and simple.

BERNARD

ANDREW

About the Artists

Andrew and Bernard Galbraith are brothers, Bernard is 20 years old and Andrew is 23. They hail from the Waterloo district in Liverpool. These versatile lads are both freelance artists and have worked together since 1987 when they had their first exhibition of wildlife paintings in oil, at Martin Mere Country Park.

They have undertaken commissions for a variety of illustrations and designs. The adventures of Yorrik is their second book. Their first was The Billy and Wally Comic Book published in 1988 and is available from the Radio Merseyside Reception. The lads are currently working on Sci Fi covers in air brush.

OTHER BOOKS BY

Pictures of Olde Liverpool.
A very high quality re-print of a 1927 book. Re-published to let everyone see or own the wonderful sketches (mostly by Herdman) of a great City's past.
ISBN 1 87226 02 7 £1.95

Scouse Passport
(just like the real thing but packed with humour and smiles) great as presents, friends abroad, retirements, business promotions etc. Can be stamped with your shop or business name as issuing officer. Well liked and well produced, good seller.
£2.50

Lancashire Halls *(Margaret Chapman)*
A complete guide to the past glories of all Lancashire Halls with pictures and sketches
Reprint at £4.95

We also distribute

Cunard — A Pictorial History £4.95 *(Maritime Museum)*

One Man And His Pan (Little N.T.'s Cookbook) £4.95 *(BBC North)*